Karela Tikkis & Garlic Tomato Chutney

Healthy Chivda

DIABETIC
SNACKS

50 to **250** Calories

TARLA DALAL

India's # 1 Cookery Author

S&C
SANJAY & CO.
MUMBAI

Third Printing : 2011

ISBN: 978-8-189491-42-0

Price: Rs. 99/-

Published & Distributed by : **Sanjay & Company**

353/ A-1, Shah & Nahar Industrial Estate, Dhanraj Mill Compound, Lower Parel (W), Mumbai - 400 013. INDIA.
Tel. : (91-22) 4345 2400 • Fax : (91-22) 2496 5876 • E-mail : sanjay@tarladalal.com • Website : www.tarladalal.com

UK and USA customers can call us on :
UK : 02080029533 • USA : 213-634-1406
For books, Membership on **tarladalal.com**, Subscription for **Cooking & More** and Recipe queries
Timing : Monday to Friday 9.30 a.m. to 6.00 p.m. (IST) and Saturday 9.30 a.m. to 1.30 p.m. (IST)
Local call charges applicable

Recipe Research & Production Design	Nutritionists	Photography	Designed by	Copy Editing
Arati Fedane	Nisha Katira	Jignesh Jhaveri	Satyamangal Rege	Ashvina Vakil
Ritika Rajpal	Sapna Kamdar			
Vibhuti Punjabi	**Food Styling**	**Typesetting**	**Printed by :**	
	Shubhangi Dhaimade	Adityas Enterprises	Minal Sales Agencies, Mumbai	

BULK PURCHASES : Tarla Dalal Cookbooks are ideal gifts. If you are interested in buying more than 500 assorted copies of Tarla Dalal Cookbooks at special prices, please contact us at 91-22-4345 2400 or email : sanjay@tarladalal.com

INTRODUCTION

Continuing in our health series is this handy little book on snacks for diabetics. If you suffer from diabetes you have to make sure that your blood glucose levels do not dip suddenly or veer too far from normal. This happens if you don't eat for fairly long intervals of time. To prevent low blood sugar (hypoglycaemia), especially if you suffer from type 1 diabetes or insulin-requiring type 2 diabetes, you must eat regular small meals at frequent intervals. The point is not to indiscriminately eat fat-laden store-bought goodies but choose from a selection of home-cooked snacks made in less oil and out of diabetes-friendly ingredients.

In this book, my team of nutritionists and I have created five categories of healthy low calorie snacks for people with diabetes: *Everyday Snacks, Occasional Treats, Light Snacks, Jar Snacks, and Accompaniments*. Each section has recipes with ingredients that are beneficial for diabetes, such as soyabean, garlic, bitter gourd (*karela*), and low fat milk and milk products like curds, *paneer* etc.

Since it is important to control the number of calories you consume everyday, each recipe is also accompanied with a "Suggested Serving Size Per Person" so you can choose from the range of appetising snacks, which provide calories ranging from 50 to 250 and modify your consumption accordingly. If you make a clever choice, you will be able to enjoy a variety of different snacks without guilt.

So go ahead, try out these snacks, which include modified favourites like *Moong Dal Idlis, page 10,* and the more unusual *Buckwheat Pancakes, page 12, Soya Poha, page 16, Jamun Smoothie, page 71 and Spicy Phudina Khakhras, page 90.* For those with a sweet tooth, we've also included a healthy version of *Chocolate Pinwheels, page 56* and exotic *Soya Cinnamon Custard with Fruits, page 73!*

Happy snacking!

Tarla Dalal

CONTENTS

EVERYDAY SNACKS

OCCASIONAL TREATS

EVERYDAY SNACKS

This section includes a range of easy-to-make snacks that can be had on a daily basis. To ensure that diabetics don't have to refrain from eating popular rice-based snacks like *idlis, dosa and poha,* I have modified them to use healthy alternatives such as *moong dal,* wheat flour and soya granules respectively. Similarly bread made from refined flour is a no-no for diabetics and has been replaced with whole wheat bread. High fat *paneer* has been substituted with low fat *paneer* in recipes such as **Spicy Paneer on Toast, page 30.**

Try to introduce diabetic-friendly ingredients like soyabean, *karela, nachni,* and whole wheat flour into your daily diet through recipes such as **Masala Wheat Dosa, page 18, Karela Tikkis, page 22, Soyabean Pancakes, page 24 and Stuffed Nachni Rotis, page 26.**

These snacks have been put together to provide **just 100-150 calories per serving,** and I have specifically cut down the amount of oil required for cooking. My team of nutritionists has also made serving suggestions that you should scrupulously follow. **For example you can have 2 idlis with 1 tbsp Healthy Coconut Chutney (150 calories) or 1 serving of Soya Poha (112 calories) etc.**

❄ *Moong Dal Idlis* ❄

South Indian snacks, while mostly nutritious, are not always suitable for those with high blood sugar. This diabetes-friendly version of idli replaces rice with wholesome moong dal and vegetables. Relish this popular snack with sizzling hot sambhar or Healthy Coconut Chutney.

Preparation time: 10 minutes.   Cooking time: 10 to 12 minutes.   Makes 12 *idlis*.
Soaking time: Overnight.

1 cup green *moong dal* (split green gram)
3 tbsp grated carrots
3 tbsp grated cabbage
1 tbsp ginger-green chilli paste
2 tsp *besan* (Bengal gram flour)
2 tbsp finely chopped coriander (*dhania*)
1 tsp fruit salt, refer handy tip
Salt to taste

Other ingredients
½ tsp oil for greasing

For serving
4 tbsp Healthy Coconut Chutney, page 97

10

1. Roast the *moong dal* in a non-stick pan till all the raw smell disappears. Cool and soak in water overnight.
2. Next day, drain and discard the water. Grind the *dal* in a mixer to a thick paste using little water if required.
3. Add the carrots, cabbage, ginger-green chilli paste, *besan*, coriander and salt and mix well.
4. Sprinkle the fruit salt on it and then a few drops of water on the fruit salt.
5. When the bubbles form, mix gently.
6. Pour the mixture gently into greased *idli* moulds and steam in a steamer for 10 to 12 minutes till they are done.
   Serve hot with healthy coconut chutney.

Handy tips: 1. Fruit salt is available at chemist shops and provision stores under the brand name ENO.
2. The *idli* is done when a toothpick or knife inserted in its centre comes out clean.

Nutritive values per *idli* with 1 tbsp healthy coconut chutney

Energy	Protein	Carbohydrates	Fat	Calcium	Folic Acid	Fibre
75 cal	3.3 gm	8.3 gm	1.8 gm	13.9 mg	19.5 mcg	0.2 gm

Buckwheat Pancakes ❄

Pancakes are favourites across the world. In this Indianised version, the not-so-common buckwheat combines with sour low fat curds and vegetables to make iron and fibre-rich pancakes. Have it along with tangy carrot garlic chutney for a delicious treat.

Preparation time: 20 minutes. Cooking time: 40 minutes.
Makes 4 small pancakes. Soaking time: 1 hour.

1 cup buckwheat (*kutto / kutti no daro*)
¼ cup sour low fat curds (*dahi*), page 101
mixed with 2 tbsp water
½ cup grated white pumpkin (*lauki / doodhi*)
1 tsp ginger-green chilli paste
2 tbsp chopped coriander (*dhania*)
A pinch turmeric powder (*haldi*)
1 tsp fruit salt (optional)
1 tsp mustard seeds (*rai / sarson*)

A pinch asafoetida (*hing*)
Salt to taste
1 tsp oil

For serving
4 tbsp Carrot Garlic Chutney, page 99

1. Wash the buckwheat once and combine it with the curds in a large bowl and mix well. Allow it to stand for 1 hour.
2. Coarsely grind the buckwheat and curds mixture in a mixer and keep aside.
3. Add the white pumpkin, ginger-green chilli paste, coriander, turmeric powder and salt and mix well. Keep the batter aside.
4. Heat the oil in a non-stick pan and add the mustard seeds. When they crackle, add the asafoetida and pour into the batter.
5. Sprinkle the fruit salt on it and then a few drops of water on the fruit salt.
6. When the bubbles form, mix gently.
7. Pour ¼ of the batter on a non-stick pan and spread an even layer to make a pancake of 100 mm. (4") diameter and cover the pan.
8. Allow it to cook for 5 to 7 minutes on a slow flame till the bottom is golden brown in colour.
9. Lift the pancake gently and turn it over to the other side.
10. Cook for another 4 to 5 minutes.
11. Repeat with remaining ingredients to make 3 more pancakes.
    Serve hot with carrot garlic chutney.

Nutritive values per small pancake with 1 tbsp carrot garlic chutney

Energy	Protein	Carbohydrates	Fat	Iron	Fibre
153 cal	4.6 gm	25.7 gm	2.2 gm	5.8 mg	3.3 gm

❁ *Adai* ❁

Easy to make and best as a snack! This South Indian preparation traditionally calls for more amount of rice, however I made it with just 2 tbsp rice and lots of dals so that you can enjoy it often without worrying about rising blood sugar levels!

Preparation time: 10 minutes. Cooking time: 40 minutes. Makes 8 *adais*.
Soaking time: 2 hours.

2 tbsp uncooked rice
3 tbsp *masoor dal* (split red lentil)
3 tbsp green *moong dal* (split green gram)
1 tbsp *urad dal* (split black lentils)
1 tsp fenugreek (*methi*) seeds
A pinch asafoetida (*hing*)
2 green chillies, finely chopped
½ tsp grated ginger
2 tbsp finely chopped coriander (*dhania*)

14

2 tsp oil
Salt to taste

For serving
4 tbsp Garlic Tomato Chutney, page 95

1. Wash and soak the rice, *dals* and fenugreek seeds in water in separate vessels for 2 hours. Drain and keep aside.
2. Combine the rice, *dals*, fenugreek seeds and asafoetida along with enough water and blend in a mixer to a smooth paste.
3. Add the green chillies, ginger, coriander, salt and a little water if required and mix well.
4. Heat a non-stick pan and grease it lightly with oil.
5. Spread 2 tbsp of the batter to form an *adai* of 100 mm (4") diameter.
6. Cook on both sides till golden brown using a little oil.
7. Repeat with the remaining batter to make 7 more *adais*.
   Serve hot with garlic tomato chutney.

Nutritive values per *adai* with 1 tbsp garlic tomato chutney

Energy	Protein	Carbohydrates	Fat	Calcium	Zinc	Fibre
72 cal	3.1 gm	9.4 gm	1.4 gm	11.2 mg	0.4 mg	0.1 gm

❀ *Soya Poha* ❀

I cannot highlight the benefits of soyabeans enough! A powerhouse of nutrients, they are used here in granule form to whip up an appetising version of poha, a popular Maharashtrian snack. Eat this unusual version regularly to benefit from the goodness of soya.

Preparation time: 5 minutes.   Cooking time: 10 minutes.   Serves 4.
Soaking time: 30 minutes.

1¼ cups soya granules
1 tsp mustard seeds (*rai / sarson*)
1 tsp *urad dal* (split black lentils)
5-6 curry leaves (*kadi patta*)
¼ tsp asafoetida (*hing*)
½ cup sliced onions
1 tsp finely chopped green chillies
1 tbsp chopped coriander *(dhania)*
¼ tsp turmeric powder (*haldi*)

½ tsp chilli powder
¼ cup boiled green peas
2 tsp lemon juice
2 tsp oil
Salt to taste

For the garnish
2 tbsp chopped coriander (*dhania*)

1. Soak the soya granules in 2 cups of warm water for 30 minutes. Squeeze and keep aside.
2. Heat the oil in a non-stick pan and add the mustard seeds, *urad dal*, curry leaves and asafoetida and sauté till the seeds crackle.
3. Add the onions and green chillies and sauté till the onions turn translucent.
4. Add the coriander, turmeric powder, chilli powder and salt and mix well.
5. Add the soya granules and green peas and sauté for another 3 to 4 minutes.
6. Remove from the flame, add the lemon juice and mix well.
   Serve hot garnished with coriander.

Nutritive values per serving

Energy	Protein	Carbohydrates	Fat	Calcium	Iron	Fibre
112 cal	8.2 gm	6.7 gm	5.8 gm	49.7 mg	2.0 mg	1.1 gm

❁ *Masala Wheat Dosa* ❁

Picture on facing page.

Suggested Serving Size Per Person: 1 dosa with 1 tbsp healthy coconut chutney

Whole wheat dosas with a stuffing of green peas and paneer make an appetising snack replete with beneficial nutrients like fibre and iron. Fibre binds glucose making it slowly available to the body and preventing a quick rise in blood glucose levels. For an authentic South Indian experience serve with Healthy Coconut Chutney, page 97.

Preparation time: 10 minutes.   Cooking time: 30 minutes.   Makes 8 *dosas*.

For the *dosa* batter
1 cup whole wheat flour (*gehun ka atta*)
1 tsp rice flour (*chawal ka atta*)
1 tsp *chana dal* (split Bengal gram), soaked for ½ hour and drained
½ tsp *urad dal* (split black lentil), soaked for ½ hour and drained
¼ tsp mustard seeds (*rai / sarson*)
¼ tsp cumin seeds (*jeera*)
5 to 6 curry leaves (*kadi patta*)

MASALA WHEAT DOSA : Recipe above & ➔
HEALTHY COCONUT CHUTNEY : Recipe on page 97

1 tsp finely chopped green chillies
¼ tsp fruit salt
½ tsp oil
Salt to taste

Other ingredients
1½ tsp oil for cooking

For serving
4 tbsp Healthy Coconut Chutney, page 97

For the stuffing
1 cup boiled green peas
½ cup low fat *paneer* (cottage cheese), page 102, diced
¼ cup chopped tomatoes
½ tsp cumin seeds (*jeera*)
1 green chilli, chopped
1 tsp *chaat masala*
2 tbsp chopped coriander (*dhania*)
1 tsp oil
Salt to taste

For the stuffing
1. Heat the oil in a non-stick pan and add the cumin seeds and green chillies.
2. Add the tomatoes and sauté for 2 to 3 minutes.
3. Add the green peas, *paneer*, *chaat masala* and salt and sauté for a few more minutes.
4. Add the coriander and mix well. Divide the stuffing into 8 equal portions and keep aside.

For the *dosa* batter
1. Whisk the wheat and rice flour with enough water to make a smooth batter. Keep aside.
2. For the tempering, heat the oil in a non-stick pan and add the *chana dal, urad dal,* mustard seeds and cumin seeds.
3. When the seeds crackle, add the curry leaves and green chillies and pour it over the *dosa* batter. Mix well.
4. Sprinkle the fruit salt on it and then a few drops of water on the fruit salt.
5. When the bubbles form, mix gently. Keep aside.

How to proceed
1. Heat a non-stick pan and grease it lightly with oil.
2. Spread 2 tbsp of the batter to form a *dosa* of 100 mm (4") diameter.
3. Cook on both sides till golden brown using a little oil.
4. Place 1 portion of the stuffing on it and fold it to make a semi-circle.
5. Repeat with the remaining *dosa* batter and stuffing to make 7 more *dosas*.
   Serve hot with healthy coconut chutney.

Nutritive values per *dosa* with 1 tbsp healthy coconut chutney

Energy	Protein	Carbohydrates	Fat	Iron	Fibre
150 cal	7.1 gm	18.7 gm	3.5 gm	1.0 mg	1.1 gm

❄ Karela Tikkis ❄

Picture on page 1.

> Suggested Serving Size Per Person: 2 tikkis with 1 tbsp garlic tomato chutney

Though unpleasantly bitter, karela tops the list of diabetes-friendly foods. It contains 'gurmarin', a polypeptide that works like insulin in our body and helps to regulate blood sugar levels. Combine karela with carrots and paneer to make these surprisingly delicious tikkis.

Preparation time: 15 minutes.   Cooking time: 10 minutes.   Makes 8 *tikkis*.

½ cup grated bitter gourd (*karela*)
¾ cup grated carrots
¼ cup crumbled low fat *paneer* (cottage cheese), page 102
¾ cup boiled and mashed green peas
¼ cup whole wheat bread crumbs
3 tsp dry mango powder (*amchur*)
2 tsp finely chopped green chillies
2 tbsp chopped coriander (*dhania*)
Salt to taste

Other ingredients
1½ tsp oil for cooking

For serving
4 tbsp Garlic Tomato Chutney, page 95

1. Apply little salt to the bitter gourd and keep aside for a while. Squeeze and keep the water aside. This water can be used as given in the handy tip.
2. Combine the bitter gourd, carrots, *paneer*, green peas, bread crumbs, dry mango powder, green chillies, coriander, green peas and salt in a bowl and mix well.
3. Divide the mixture into 8 equal potions and shape into round, flat *tikkis*.
4. Cook them on a non-stick pan, using a little oil, till both sides are golden brown. Serve hot with garlic tomato chutney.

Handy tip: You will benefit from drinking the water squeezed from the *karela* as well. To cut its bitter taste, mix with a glass of water or tomato juice.

Nutritive values per *tikki* with 1 tbsp garlic tomato chutney

Energy	Protein	Carbohydrates	Fat	Vitamin A	Vitamin C	Fibre
75 cal	4.4 gm	12.2 gm	1.4 gm	377.9 mcg	8.7 mg	1.1 gm

Soyabean Pancakes

Picture on backcover.

Suggested Serving Size Per Person: 1 pancake with 1 tbsp mint and onion chutney

Rich in folic acid and calcium, soyabeans combine with whole wheat flour to make nutritious pancakes. Folic acid converts homocysteine (a harmful amino acid that causes heart diseases) into methionine, which protects the heart and reduces the risk of developing heart disorders, a long-term complication of diabetes.

Preparation time: 10 minutes.   Cooking time: 25 minutes.   Makes 6 pancakes.
Soaking time: Overnight.

1 cup soyabeans
3 tbsp whole wheat flour (*gehun ka atta*)
¼ tsp freshly ground pepper
Salt to taste

To be mixed into a topping
¾ cup finely chopped onions
2 tbsp finely chopped coriander (*dhania*)

24

2 tsp finely chopped green chillies

Other ingredients
2 tsp oil for cooking

For serving
4 tbsp Mint and Onion Chutney, page 93

1. Soak the soyabeans in water overnight. Next day wash, drain and discard the water.
2. Grind with enough water in a mixer to make a smooth batter.
3. Add the wheat flour, pepper and salt and mix well. Keep aside.
4. Heat a non-stick pan and grease it lightly with oil.
5. Spread 2 tbsp of the batter to form a pancake of 125 mm (5") diameter.
6. Spread 1 tbsp of the topping on it and press it gently so it sticks to the pancake.
7. Cook on both sides till golden brown using a little oil.
8. Repeat with the remaining batter and topping to make 5 more pancakes.
   Serve hot with mint and onion chutney.

Nutritive values per pancake with 1 tbsp mint and onion chutney

Energy	Protein	Carbohydrates	Fat	Calcium	Folic Acid	Fibre
141 cal	**11.0 gm**	10.0 gm	6.4 gm	**68.5 mg**	**26.3 mcg**	**1.1 gm**

Stuffed Nachni Rotis

Make scrumptious rotis out of nachni and wheat flour and enjoy them with fresh low fat curds or a glass of sugar-free juice. The karela in the vegetable stuffing provides additional benefits for diabetics, while the cauliflower offsets the bitterness.

Preparation time: 10 minutes.   Cooking time: 20 minutes.   Makes 4 *rotis*.

For the dough
¼ cup *nachni / ragi* (red millet) flour
¼ cup whole wheat flour (*gehun ka atta*)
1 tsp oil
Salt to taste

To be mixed into a stuffing
½ cup grated cauliflower
3 tbsp finely chopped fenugreek (*methi*) leaves
2 tbsp grated bitter gourd (*karela*)

¼ tsp finely chopped green chillies
¼ tsp finely chopped ginger
Salt to taste

Other ingredients
2 tsp oil for cooking
Whole wheat flour (*gehun ka atta*)
for rolling

For the dough
1. Combine all the ingredients and knead into soft dough, using enough warm water.
2. Divide the dough into 4 equal portions and keep aside.

How to proceed
1. Divide the stuffing into 4 equal portions. Keep aside.
2. Roll out one portion of the dough into a circle of 75 mm. (3") diameter using a little flour.
3. Place 2 tbsp of the filling in the center of the circle.
4. Bring together all the sides in the center and seal tightly.
5. Roll out again into a circle of 125 mm. (5") diameter using a little flour.
6. Cook on a non-stick pan, using a ½ tsp oil, until both sides are golden brown.
7. Repeat with the remaining dough and stuffing to make 3 more stuffed *rotis*. Serve hot.

Nutritive values per *roti*

Energy	Protein	Carbohydrates	Fat	Vitamin C	Iron
76 cal	1.8 gm	10.6 gm	4.0 gm	10.6 mg	0.8 mg

❄ *Bermi Parathas* ❄

Suggested Serving Size Per Person: 1½ parathas

Who can resist a scrumptious paratha? An ideal snack option which can also make a filling meal. In this version, spring onions provide crunch to a wholesome and appetising stuffing of moong dal.

Preparation time: 20 minutes.   Cooking time: 20 minutes.   Makes 6 *parathas*.

For the dough
1 cup whole wheat flour (*gehun ka atta*)
Salt to taste

To be mixed into a stuffing
3 tbsp green *moong dal* (split green gram), soaked overnight and drained
¼ cup finely chopped spring onions (including greens)
1 tsp chilli powder
1 tsp cumin seeds (*jeera*) powder
¼ tsp asafoetida (*hing*)
Salt to taste

Other ingredients
Whole wheat flour (*gehun ka atta*)
for rolling
2 tsp oil for cooking

28

For the dough
1. Combine the wheat flour and salt and knead into soft dough using enough water.
2. Divide the dough into 6 equal portions. Keep aside.

How to proceed
1. Roll out each portion of the dough into a circle of 75 mm (3") diameter.
2. Place one portion of the stuffing mixture in the centre of the circle.
3. Bring together all the sides in the centre and seal tightly.
4. Roll out again into a circle of 100 mm (4") diameter, using a little whole wheat flour.
5. Cook on a hot *tava* (griddle), using a little oil, until both sides are golden brown.
6. Repeat with the remaining dough and stuffing to make 5 more *parathas*.
   Serve hot.

Handy tip: 3 tbsp of raw green *moong dal* will yield approximately ½ cup soaked green *moong dal*.

Nutritive values per *paratha*

Energy	Protein	Carbohydrates	Fat	Iron	Zinc	Fibre
101 cal	3.9 gm	16.8 gm	2.1 gm	**1.2 mg**	0.6 mg	**0.5 gm**

❋ *Spicy Paneer on Toast* ❋

> Suggested Serving Size Per Person: 1 toast

A zesty topping made from low fat paneer and vegetables adds spice to nutritious whole wheat toasts. A great teatime snack, they make a good accompaniment to a hot, sugar-free beverage! Since paneer is high in protein, go easy on milk and milk products like curds for the rest of the day.

Preparation time: 10 minutes.   Cooking time: 10 minutes.   Makes 4 toasts.
Baking temperature: 200°C (400°F).   Baking time: 5 minutes.

4 slices whole wheat brown bread, toasted

For the spicy *paneer* topping
½ cup grated low fat *paneer* (cottage cheese), page 102
¼ cup finely chopped onions
½ tsp finely chopped ginger
½ tsp finely chopped garlic
2 tbsp finely chopped capsicum

1 to 2 green chillies, finely chopped
A pinch turmeric powder (*haldi*)
A pinch black salt (*sanchal*)
2 tbsp chopped coriander (*dhania*)
2 tbsp chopped mint leaves (*phudina*)
1 tsp lemon juice
1 tsp oil
Salt to taste

For the spicy *paneer* topping
1. Heat the oil in a non-stick pan, add the onions, ginger, garlic and sauté till the onions turn translucent.
2. Add the capsicum, green chillies, turmeric powder and black salt and sauté for a minute.
3. Add the *paneer*, coriander, mint leaves, lemon juice and salt and mix well.
4. Divide the topping into 4 equal portions and keep aside.

How to proceed
1. Remove the sides of the toasted bread and spread 1 portion of the spicy *paneer* mixture on each toasted bread.

2. Grill in a pre-heated oven at 200°C (400°F) for a minute.
   Serve hot.

Nutritive values per toast

Energy	Protein	Carbohydrates	Fat	Vitamin A	Iron	Fibre
147 cal	10.0 gm	22.6 gm	1.8 gm	644.6 mcg	1.0 mg	0.4 gm

OCCASIONAL TREATS

I'm sure you crave normally taboo foods such as pizzas, tortillas, pasta and cheese *parathas*! Here's a piece of good news for all the diabetics in the world. You don't have to refrain from them completely, just make sure you have them very occasionally in limited quantities. Though they contain more calories than everyday snacks, these treats have also been modified to be as healthy as possible. I have tried to use whole wheat pizza base, low fat mozzarella cheese, lots of vegetables, and cocoa powder instead of chocolate.

The recipes in this section provide **160 calories to 225 calories per serving**. A few are on the higher side calorie-wise, like *Four Seasons Pizza, page 42, Club Sandwich, page 49.* Some, while not very high in calories, include ingredients like pasta such as *Chunky Tomato Pasta, page 47,* or cocoa powder in *Chocolate Pinwheels, page 56,* and must be consumed in restricted amounts and only once in 15 days.

Suggested Serving Size Per Person so you may find that while you can eat **4 slices of pizza, only 1 sandwich, or a small serving of pasta is recommended.** Try not to cheat so that you stay within your specified limit of 225 calories.

❄ *Creamy Mushroom Tartlets* ❄

> Suggested Serving Size Per Person: 2 tartlets

An innovative option for a special tea party. Fill these easy-to-make whole wheat bread tartlets with delicious low calorie dieter's white sauce that is healthy without compromising on taste. Mushrooms add flavour and texture to this wonderful snack!

Preparation time: 25 minutes.   Cooking time: 20 minutes.   Makes 8 tartlets.
Baking temperature: 230°C (460°F).   Baking time: 20 minutes.

For the tartlets cases
8 slices whole wheat bread
1½ tsp melted low fat butter

For the dieter's white sauce (approx. makes 1 cup)
¾ cup chopped cauliflower or white pumpkin (*lauki / doodhi*)
2 tsp whole wheat flour (*gehun ka atta*)
½ cup low fat milk

1 tsp low fat butter
Salt and freshly ground pepper to taste

For the creamy mushroom sauce
1½ cups sliced mushrooms (*khumbh*)
3 tbsp chopped onions
1 tsp finely chopped garlic
½ tsp finely chopped green chillies
1 cup dieter's white sauce, recipe sideways
2 tsp oil
Salt and freshly ground pepper to taste.

Other ingredients
8 tsp grated mozzarella cheese

For the tartlet cases
1. Remove the crust from the bread slices.
2. Roll each slice with a rolling pin.
3. Press the rolled slices into the cavities of a muffin tray that is lightly greased with butter.
4. Brush with the remaining melted butter and bake in a pre-heated oven at 230°C (460°F) for 8 to 10 minutes or until crisp. Keep aside.

For the dieter's white sauce
1. Boil the cauliflower in 1 cup of water until soft. Blend in a mixer to a smooth purée. Strain and keep aside.
2. Heat the butter in a non-stick pan, add the flour and cook for ½ a minute.
3. Add the milk and cauliflower purée and heat while stirring continuously till the sauce thickens.
4. Add the salt and pepper and mix well. Keep aside.

For the creamy mushroom sauce
1. Heat the oil in a non-stick pan, add the onions and sauté till they turn translucent.

2. Add the garlic, green chillies and mushrooms and sauté till the mushrooms become soft.
3. Add the dieter's white sauce, salt and pepper and mix well.
4. Simmer for 1 to 2 minutes and keep aside.

How to proceed
1. Fill 2½ tbsp of the creamy mushroom sauce in each tartlet and sprinkle 1 tsp cheese on top.
2. Bake in a pre-heated oven at 230°C (460°F) for a few minutes or till the cheese melts. Serve hot.

Handy tip: You can store the left over dieter's white sauce for making other recipes. Store it in an air-tight container in a refrigerator, it will stay for 1-2 days.

Nutritive values per tartlet

Energy	Protein	Carbohydrates	Fat	Calcium	Iron	Fibre
89 cal	3.4 gm	12.5 gm	2.8 gm	43.1 mg	0.7 mg	0.5 gm

SPINACH TARTLETS : Recipe on page 38. ↪

❀ *Spinach Tartlets* ❀

Picture on page 37.

> Suggested Serving Size Per Person: 2 tartlets

A simple, less exotic spinach filling for the whole wheat tartlets referred to earlier. The dieter's white sauce keeps the snack healthy. For a tea party, you can create a range of different fillings. Remember however to go easy on the mozzarella cheese even if it is low in calories than other types of processed cheese.

Preparation time: 10 minutes.   Cooking time: 15 to 20 minutes.   Makes 8 tartlets.
Baking temperature: 230°C (460°F).   Baking time: 8 to 10 minutes.

8 whole wheat bread tartlet cases, page 34

For the spinach filling
2½ cups chopped spinach (*palak*)
¼ cup chopped onions
½ tsp chopped green chillies
¼ cup dieter's white sauce, page 34
1 tsp oil
Salt to taste

Other ingredients
8 tsp grated mozzarella cheese

For the spinach filling
1. Heat the oil in a non-stick pan, add the onions and sauté till they turn translucent. Add the green chillies and fry again for a few seconds.
2. Add the spinach and cook for 2 minutes. Drain.
3. Add the dieter's white sauce and salt and mix well.
4. Cook until the mixture becomes thick. Remove from the flame and keep aside.

How to proceed
1. Fill 2½ tbsp spinach mixture in each tartlet and sprinkle 1 tsp of cheese on top.
2. Bake in a pre-heated oven at 230°C (460°F) for a few minutes or till the cheese melts.
   Serve hot.

Nutritive values per tartlet

Energy	Protein	Carbohydrates	Fat	Vitamin A	Calcium	Folic Acid	Fibre
85 cal	3.2 gm	11.6 gm	2.3 gm	**1079.8 mcg**	**44.7 mg**	**31.6 mcg**	0.4 gm

✿ *Capsicum and Cheese Parathas* ✿

Healthy parathas are actually possible! Make this unusual stuffing with low calorie, low fat mozzarella cheese and capsicum. 1½ serving of these filling parathas when you're feeling peckish will keep you going till the next meal!

Preparation time: 20 minutes.   Cooking time: 25 minutes.   Makes 5 *parathas*.

For the dough
1 cup whole wheat flour (*gehun ka atta*)
A pinch salt

To be mixed into a stuffing
¾ cup thinly sliced capsicum
⅓ cup grated mozzarella cheese
½ tsp chilli powder
½ tsp coriander (*dhania*) powder
¼ tsp *chaat masala*

2 tbsp finely chopped coriander (*dhania*)
Salt to taste

Other ingredients
Whole wheat flour (*gehun ka atta*) for rolling
1½ tsp oil for cooking

For the dough
1. Combine the wheat flour, salt and enough water to make a soft dough.
2. Knead well, cover with a wet muslin cloth and keep aside for 20 minutes.
3. Divide the dough into 10 equal portions. Keep aside.

How to proceed
1. Divide the prepared stuffing into 5 equal portions and keep aside.
2. Roll out 2 portions of the dough into a circle of 125 mm. (5") diameter, using a little flour for rolling.
3. Place 1 circle on a flat surface, spread 1 portion of the stuffing evenly on it and cover with another circle. Press lightly to seal the edges well.
4. Cook on a non-stick pan, using ½ tsp oil, until brown spots appear on both the sides.
5. Repeat with the remaining dough and stuffing to make 4 more *parathas*.
   Serve hot.

Nutritive values per *paratha*

Energy	Protein	Carbohydrates	Fat	Calcium	Zinc	Fibre
105 cal	3.8 gm	15.5 gm	3.1 gm	41.2 mg	0.6 mg	0.5 gm

❁ Four Seasons Pizza ❁

An innovative but time-consuming snack that is well worth the extra trouble! Use whole wheat pizza bases and a range of exciting but low calorie toppings to create this colourful pizza. Remember not to indulge in it too often, however tempting it may look and taste! Make it a special treat.

Preparation time: 25 minutes.   Cooking time: 15 minutes.   Makes 16 slices.
Baking temperature: 200°C (400°F).   Baking time: 45 minutes.

2 whole wheat pizza bases, [200 mm. (8")] diameter
1/3 cup grated mozzarella cheese

For the pizza sauce
¼ cup tomato purée
¼ cup chopped tomatoes
2 bayleaves (*tejpatta*)
4 to 6 peppercorns

¼ cup chopped onions
1 tsp chopped garlic
½ capsicum, deseeded
1 tsp sugar
½ tsp dried oregano
2 tsp olive oil / oil
Salt to taste

For the topping
4 slices sun-dried tomatoes
1 tsp chopped garlic
4 tomato slices
1 tbsp chopped olives
¼ cup blanched and sliced mushrooms (*khumbh*)
2 tbsp blanched and chopped spinach (*palak*)
2 tbsp chopped capsicum
2 tbsp cooked yellow corn kernels (*makai ke dane*)

For the pizza sauce
1. Heat the oil in a non-stick pan, add the bayleaves and peppercorns and sauté for a few seconds.
2. Add the onions, garlic and capsicum and sauté for a few minutes.

3. Add the tomato purée, 2 tbsp water, sugar and salt and simmer for 10 to 15 minutes until the sauce reduces a little.
4. Finally, add the oregano and mix well. Remove the bayleaves, peppercorns and capsicum and discard. Keep aside.

How to proceed
1. Place one pizza base on a baking tray.
2. Spread half the tomato sauce on it. Divide the base into 4 equal portions.
3. On one portion, place two sun-dried tomato slices and sprinkle half the garlic on it.
4. On one portion, place two tomato slices and sprinkle half the chopped olives.
5. On one portion, place half the mushroom slices and spread half of the spinach on it.
6. Mix capsicum and corn together and place half of the mixture on the last portion of the base.
7. Sprinkle half the cheese on top and bake in a pre-heated oven at 200°C (400°F) for 20 minutes or until the base is evenly browned and the cheese melts.
8. Repeat with the remaining ingredients to make another pizza.
9. Just before serving cut each pizza into 8 equal slices. Serve hot.

Nutritive values per slice

Energy	Protein	Carbohydrates	Fat	Vitamin A	Fibre
60 cal	2.5 gm	11.1 gm	1.6 gm	194.5 mcg	0.5 gm

❁ *Paneer Veggie Wrap* ❁

Easy-to-make and pleasing to the palate. Use leftover chapattis to make innovative wraps with a crunchy vegetable filling. Much healthier than those made with refined flour (maida), the wraps provide ample nutrients such as protein, calcium, iron and zinc.

Preparation time: 10 minutes.   Cooking time: 20 minutes.   Makes 4 wraps.

4 left over *chapattis,* approx. 125 mm. (5") in diameter

To be mixed into filling
½ cup low fat grated *paneer* (cottage cheese), page 102
½ cup grated cabbage
½ cup grated carrots
2 tsp finely chopped green chillies
3 tbsp chopped coriander (*dhania*)
Salt to taste

Other ingredients
2 tsp low fat butter for cooking

1. Divide the filling into 4 equal portions and keep aside.
2. Place 1 *chapatti* on a clean dry surface.
3. Put 3 tbsp of the filling at one end of the *chapatti* and roll it up tightly.
4. Repeat with the remaining *chapattis* and filling to make 3 more wraps.
5. Just before serving, grill the wraps in a pre-heated sandwich griller using a little low fat butter till they become crisp and pink spots appear on the surface. Serve immediately.

Nutritive values per wrap

Energy	Protein	Carbohydrates	Fat	Calcium	Iron	Zinc	Fibre
144 cal	10.0 gm	22.5 gm	1.4 gm	360.9 mg	0.9 mg	0.4 mg	0.5 gm

❀ *Chunky Tomato Pasta* ❀

Pasta is not usually recommended for diabetics. However, unlike the usual calorie-laden and creamy pasta dishes, this delicacy makes use lots of tomatoes, vegetables and just a dash of low fat cream to satisfy your cravings. One serving of pasta, though small, is just enough to relish as a snack.

Preparation time: 20 minutes.   Cooking time: 15 minutes.   Serves 4.

2 cups cooked farfalle (bow-shaped pasta)
6 medium tomatoes, blanched
3 large cloves garlic, finely chopped
1 tbsp finely chopped celery
1 tsp chopped fresh basil
1 tbsp low fat cream
1 tsp sugar
½ cup broccoli florets, blanched
2 tsp olive oil

Salt and freshly ground pepper to taste

1. Cut the blanched tomatoes into halves and deseed.
2. Cut each half into 3 chunks lengthwise and keep aside.
3. Heat the oil in a non-stick pan, add the garlic and celery and fry for a few seconds.
4. Add the tomato chunks, basil, salt and pepper and mix well.
5. Add the cream and sugar and mix well. Remove from the flame and keep aside.
6. Just before serving, add the pasta and broccoli and toss well.
   Serve immediately.

Handy tip: 1¼ cups of uncooked farfelle will approximately yield 2 cups of cooked pasta.

Nutritive values per serving

Energy	Protein	Carbohydrates	Fat	Vitamin A	Vitamin C	Fibre
164 cal	4.9 gm	26.2 gm	4.6 gm	**715.3 mcg**	**40.6 mg**	**2.0 gm**

❁ Club Sandwich ❁

Picture on cover.

> Suggested Serving Size Per Person: 1 sandwich

This truly unusual combination of whole wheat toast and traditional chilas makes a satiating snack. Mint and Onion Chutney adds an extra zing to this layered vegetable club sandwich with a difference. Make it the next time you are seeking a fusion of the east and west!

Preparation time: 10 minutes.   Cooking time: 10 minutes.   Makes 2 sandwiches.

6 slices whole wheat bread, toasted
2 tbsp Mint and Onion Chutney, page 93

For the filling
2 lettuce leaves
8 slices unpeeled cucumber
8 slices tomatoes
2 *chilas*, page 50

For the *chilas*
2 tbsp whole wheat flour *(gehun ka atta)*
1½ tbsp *besan* (Bengal gram flour)
1½ tbsp *jowar* (white millet) flour
3 tbsp chopped onions
¼ cup chopped tomatoes
2 tbsp chopped coriander *(dhania)*
1 green chilli, finely chopped
Salt to taste

Other ingredients
1 tsp oil for cooking

For the *chilas*
1. Mix together all the ingredients in a bowl and add enough water to make a smooth batter and divide into 2 equal portions.
2. Heat a non-stick pan and grease it lightly with oil.
3. Spread one portion of the batter on it to form a thick round *chila* of 100 mm (4") diameter.
4. Cook on both sides till golden brown, using a little oil.
5. Repeat with the remaining batter to make 1 more *chila*. Keep aside.

How to proceed

1. Apply little *chutney* on all the toasted bread slices and keep aside.
2. Place a toasted bread slice on a flat dry surface, put one *chila* on it. Cover with another toasted bread slice with the chutney side facing up.
3. Place a lettuce leaf, 4 slices cucumber and 4 slices of tomatoes on it and cover with the third toasted bread slice.
4. Repeat with the remaining ingredients to make 1 more sandwich.
5. Cut each sandwich into 4 equal portions and serve immediately.

Handy Tip: These days uncut whole wheat bread loaves are available at bakeries. Cut these into thin slices and use them instead of the regular pre-sliced bread, as then the calories and carbohydrates will be reduced.

Nutritive values per sandwich

Energy	Protein	Carbohydrates	Fat	Vitamin A	Iron	Fibre
246 cal	9.2 gm	48.0 gm	4.1 gm	499.0 mcg	3.1 mg	1.7 gm

❃ Veggie Stuffed Tortillas ❃

Wheat flour replaces maize flour in this healthier version of tortillas, making it more suited for people with high blood sugar. Stuff this Mexican staple with lots of crunchy vegetables to make a balanced snack with enough vitamin C to fight against free radicals and prevent diabetes-related complications.

Preparation time: 35 minutes.   Cooking time: 35 minutes.   Makes 6 tortillas.

For the tortillas
½ cup whole wheat flour (*gehun ka atta*)
¼ cup *maida* (plain flour)
1 tsp oil
½ tsp salt

For the veggie stuffing
½ cup sliced onions
½ chopped spring onions

½ cup shredded cabbage
¼ cup sliced capsicum
1 tomato, cut into slices
2 tbsp coarsely grated carrots
2 tbsp bean sprouts
½ cup grated low fat *paneer* (cottage cheese), page 102
1 tsp soya sauce
½ tsp ginger juice

52

1 tsp chilli-garlic paste
2 tsp chillies in vinegar
2 tsp oil
Salt to taste

Other ingredients
Whole wheat flour (*gehun ka atta*) for rolling

For the tortillas
1. Mix the flours, oil and salt and make a dough by adding enough warm water.
2. Knead the dough well, cover with a wet cloth and keep aside for ½ an hour. Knead again and divide it into 6 equal portions.
3. Roll out the each portion into thin rounds of 100 mm (5") diameter with the help of a little flour.
4. Cook lightly on a non-stick pan and keep aside.

For the veggie stuffing
1. Heat the oil in a non-stick pan on a high flame, add the vegetables and bean sprouts and stir-fry for a few minutes.
2. Add the *paneer*, soya sauce, ginger juice, chilli-garlic paste, chillies in vinegar and salt and toss well.
3. Divide the stuffing into 6 equal portions and keep aside.

How to proceed

1. Place 1 tortilla on a flat dry surface and spread 1 portion of the stuffing on it.
2. Fold into a semi-circle and serve immediately.
3. Repeat with the remaining tortillas and stuffing to make 5 more veggie stuffed tortillas.

Handy Tips

1. You can make large quantities of tortillas and freeze them in a refrigerator in an air-tight container or wrapped in a plastic film. These can be defrosted and used when hunger pangs strike.
2. To make chilli-garlic paste just grind 5 to 6 garlic cloves with 5 whole dry red chillies and 2 tbsp of water.
3. You can cut 3 to 4 green chillies and add to ½ cup of white vinegar to make chillies in vinegar and store it in refrigerator for many days.

Nutritive values per tortilla

Energy	Protein	Carbohydrates	Fat	Vitamin C	Calcium	Fibre
164 cal	9.6 gm	24.6 gm	3.0 gm	**17.8 mg**	**259.7 mg**	**1.0 gm**

BRUSCHETTAS WITH TOMATO AND BASIL : Recipe on page 62. →

❁ *Chocolate Pinwheels* ❁

Suggested Serving Size Per Person: 4 pinwheels

Cocoa powder is a good substitute for high calorie chocolate sauce in these attractive pinwheels. Enjoy this scrumptious snack once in 15 days to satisfy your sweet tooth. Try to keep it for special occasions like a party and remember not to go overboard.

Preparation time: 10 minutes.   Cooking time: 5 to 7 minutes.
Makes 12 pinwheels.

4 slices whole wheat bread
4 tsp roasted quick rolled oats

For the chocolate spread (makes 8 tbsp approx.)
1 tbsp low fat butter
2 tbsp cocoa powder
5 tbsp low fat milk
1 tsp sugar substitute

For the chocolate spread
1. Melt the butter in a non-stick pan, add the cocoa powder and cook for a minute while stirring continuously.
2. Add the milk and sugar substitute and cook while still stirring continuously till it thickens. Keep aside.

How to proceed
1. Take a bread slice and cut its sides. Apply 2 tbsp of the spread and sprinkle 1 tsp of oats evenly on the slice and roll up like a Swiss roll.
2. Cut it into 3 equal portions.
3. Repeat with the remaining bread slices and chocolate spread to make 9 more pinwheels.
   Serve immediately.

Handy Tip: Use fresh bread slices for this recipe. If you still have trouble rolling, wrap them in a moist muslin cloth and steam them in a steamer for 2 minutes. Then apply the spread and proceed as required.

Nutritive values per pinwheel

Energy	Protein	Carbohydrates	Fat	Calcium	Fibre
27 cal	1.0 gm	4.2 gm	0.7 gm	**13.4 mg**	**0.1 gm**

Moong Dal Waffles with Stir-Fried Vegetables

> Suggested Serving Size Per Person: 1 waffle

An Indian touch to western waffles! Moong dal provides folic acid while vegetables ensure fibre in this unusual yet delicious combination. Make the waffles in advance and rustle up the colourful stir-fried vegetables just before you need them.

Preparation time: 10 minutes. Cooking time: 15 minutes. Makes 4 waffles.
Soaking time: 3 to 4 hours.

For the waffles
1 cup green *moong dal* (split green gram) with skin
2 to 3 green chillies, finely chopped
2 tbsp chopped fenugreek (*methi*) leaves
2 tsp *besan* (Bengal gram flour)
A pinch asafoetida (*hing*)
¼ tsp fruit salt
2 pinches sugar (optional)
2 tsp oil

58

Salt to taste

For the stir-fried vegetables
½ cup capsicum, cut into thin strips
1 spring onion, thinly sliced
½ cup baby corn, thinly sliced
½ thinly sliced cucumber
½ cup broccoli florets
1 small tomato, deseeded and sliced
¼ cup bean sprouts
1 tsp onion seeds (*kalonji*)
1 tsp oil
Salt to taste

For the waffles
1. Soak the *moong dal* in water for 3 to 4 hours. Wash, drain and discard the water.
2. Grind the soaked *dal* with green chillies and little water in a mixer to get a smooth batter.
3. Add the fenugreek leaves, *besan*, asafoetida, fruit salt, sugar, oil and salt and mix well.
4. Pour a ladleful of batter in a pre-heated waffle iron and bake until crisp.

5. Repeat with the remaining batter to make 3 more waffles. Keep aside.

For the stir-fried vegetables
1. Heat the oil in a non-stick pan and add the onion seeds.
2. When the seeds crackle, add all the vegetables, bean sprouts and salt and sauté on a high flame till the vegetables are tender.
3. Remove from the flame, divide it into 4 equal portions and keep aside.

How to proceed
Place the waffles in individual serving dishes, top them each with a portion of the stir-fried vegetables and serve immediately.

Nutritive values per waffle

Energy	Protein	Carbohydrates	Fat	Folic acid	Zinc	Fibre
215 cal	11.8 gm	32.9 gm	4.5 gm	72.0 mcg	1.4 mg	1.5 gm

LIGHT SNACKS

Diabetics are always advised by nutritionist to eat frequent small meals and you need a choice of snacks that offer not more than **50-75 calories per serving**. Remember these are not meant to replace meals or everyday snacks; they're just to keep you going till the next one! So try these interesting low calorie snacks instead to help stave off mid-morning and mid-evening hunger pangs. Raw fruits and salads can get boring after a while hence salads, juices, stir-fries, and even *bhel* made from diabetes-friendly ingredients like sprouts, *jamun*, soya beans, cinnamon, etc are included in this section.

Servings sizes are small, such as *2 Bruschettas with Tomato and Basil, page 62* or *1 serving of Nutritious Bhel, page 67* or **a small glass of** *Jamun Smoothie, page 71*.

❄ *Bruschettas with Tomato and Basil* ❄

Picture on page 55.

Suggested Serving Size Per Person: 4 pieces

This Italian favourite is a great any-time snack. Basil and tomatoes add subtle flavour and texture to this easy-to-make snack that tots up just 38 calories per piece! Have a couple of pieces to satisfy mid-morning or mid-evening hunger pangs.

Preparation time: 10 minutes.   Cooking time: 5 minutes.   Makes 20 pieces.
Baking temperature: 180°C (360°F).   Baking time: 8 to 10 minutes.

5 slices whole wheat bread
2 tsp olive oil
2 cloves garlic, finely chopped

For the topping (approx. makes 1 cup)
5 medium tomatoes
1 tbsp chopped fresh basil leaves
1 tsp dried oregano
Salt and freshly ground pepper to taste

62

For the topping
1. Cut each tomato into half lengthwise and gently remove all the seeds and pulp.
2. Finely chop the tomatoes, add in all the other ingredients and mix well.
3. Keep aside for at least 10 to 15 minutes.
4. Drain out the excess liquid. Keep aside.

How to proceed
1. Brush some olive oil and garlic onto each bread slice, cut them diagonally into two and bake in a pre-heated oven at 180°C (360°F) for 3 to 4 minutes till they are lightly toasted.
2. Top each toasted piece with 1½ tbsp of the topping cut into two equal pieces and serve immediately.

Handy Tip: Use whole-wheat French bread slices if possible as it will soak the juices and taste better.

Nutritive values per piece

Energy	Protein	Carbohydrates	Fat	Calcium	Iron	Fibre
19 cal	0.6 gm	2.9 gm	0.6 gm	8.0 mg	0.3 mg	0.2 gm

❄ *Cous Cous Salad* ❄

Picture on facing page.

Suggested Serving Size Per Person: 1 serving

Cous cous is a pre-cooked wheat derivative available only in selective stores. I have used the more readily available broken wheat in this multi-textured and healthy salad, which is a great alternative to calorie-laden snacks. A delicately flavoured mint dressing perks up this nutrient-rich assortment of vegetables and dalia.

Preparation time: 15 minutes.   Cooking time: 10 minutes.   Serves 6.

½ cup broken wheat (*dalia*)
1 cup cucumber cubes
1 cup chopped tomatoes
1 cup broccoli florets
1 cup sliced mushrooms (*khumbh*)
1 cup torn lettuce

To be mixed into a dressing
¼ cup finely chopped mint leaves (*phudina*)

COUS COUS SALAD : Recipe above. ↪

1 tbsp lemon juice
Salt and freshly ground pepper to taste

Other ingredients
½ tsp oil for cooking

1. Boil vesselful of water and add the oil and salt to it.
2. Add the broken wheat and boil for 6 to 7 minutes.
3. Drain, wash with cold water and drain again.
4. Add all the remaining ingredients, pour the dressing over it and toss well.
5. Keep refrigerated for at least 1 hour.
   Serve chilled.

Nutritive values per serving

Energy	Protein	Carbohydrates	Fat	Vitamin C	Folic Acid	Fibre
64 cal	2.5 gm	12.9 gm	0.5 gm	**20.6 mg**	**19.5 mcg**	1.0 gm

❁ *Nutritious Bhel* ❁

Getting together with friends for bhel and good conversation? Puffed rice is mixed with fibre-rich sprouts and fruits that prevent blood glucose levels from fluctuating. Munch on this bhel to keep up with your daily nutrient requirements.

Preparation time: 10 minutes. Cooking time: 10 minutes. Serves 4.

For the *masala* puffed rice
1 cup puffed rice (*mamara / kurmura*)
½ tsp cumin seeds (*jeera*)
A pinch asafoetida (*hing*)
¼ tsp turmeric powder (*haldi*)
½ tsp black salt (*sanchal*)
½ tsp oil

Other ingredients
½ cup boiled mixed sprouts (*matki, moong, chana* etc.)

½ cup orange segments
½ cup chopped apples
½ cup finely chopped tomatoes
½ cup fresh pomegranate seeds (*anardana*)
3 tbsp chopped raw mango
4 tbsp chopped coriander (*dhania*)
4 tsp lemon juice
Salt to taste

For the *masala* puffed rice
1. Heat the oil in a non-stick pan and add the cumin seeds. When they crackle, add the asafoetida, turmeric powder and puffed rice. Mix well.
2. Add the black salt and mix well and cool completely.
3. Store in an air-tight container and use as required.

How to serve
Mix the *masala* puffed rice with all the other ingredients together in a bowl and serve immediately.

Nutritive values per serving

Energy	Protein	Carbohydrates	Fat	Fibre
72 cal	2.5 gm	15.7 gm	1.0 gm	**1.7 gm**

❄ *Spinach and Tofu Dip with Crackers* ❄

When you're having friends over for an early evening, serve them cream cracker biscuits with this light and healthy spinach and tofu dip. While tofu is full of benefits, if not easily available, you can use replace it with low fat paneer. Remember to make the low fat paneer from low fat milk.

Preparation time: 5 minutes.   Cooking time: 5 minutes.   Makes 18 pieces.

For the spinach and tofu dip
3 cups chopped spinach (*palak*)
¾ cup *tofu* (soya *paneer*)
¼ cup sliced onions
1 tsp lemon juice
1 tsp oregano
2 tsp oil
Salt and freshly ground pepper to taste

For serving
18 cream cracker biscuits

For the spinach and tofu dip
1. Heat the spinach in a non-stick pan and cook on a high flame for a minute to remove its moisture. Remove from the pan and keep aside.
2. Heat 1 tsp of oil in the same pan, add the onions and sauté till they turn translucent.
3. Combine the onions, spinach, tofu, lemon juice, oregano, remaining 1 tsp of oil, salt and pepper and blend in a mixer to make a thick coarse paste.
4. Keep refrigerated for atleast an hour.

How to serve
Place the cream cracker biscuits in a serving plate, top each biscuit with 1 tbsp of the dip and serve immediately.

Nutritive values per piece

Energy	Protein	Carbohydrates	Fat	Calcium	Folic Acid	Fibre
34 cal	0.9 gm	5.1 gm	1.8 gm	10.3 mg	14.0 mcg	0.3 gm

❊ *Jamun Smoothie* ❊

Diabetes-friendly jamun blends with low fat curds to make a delectable smoothie. Jambolene, the enzyme found in jamun, helps to utilise the glucose in the body thereby inhibiting the unwanted rise in the blood glucose levels. Try to include as much jamun in your diet as possible it's very good for you.

Preparation time: 10 minutes.   Cooking time: Nil.   Makes 3 small glasses.

¾ cup deseeded and chopped black *jamun*
2 cups low fat curds (*dahi*), page 101
1 tsp sugar substitute
½ cup crushed ice

1. Mix together all the ingredients and blend in a mixer till smooth.
2. Pour the smoothie into 3 small glasses and serve immediately.

Handy tip: Use slightly overripe *jamun* to cut down on the amount of sugar substitute needed. Buy large quantities of *jamun* when in season, and pulp and store them in the freezer for months.

Nutritive values per small glass

Energy	Protein	Carbohydrates	Fat	Vitamin A	Vitamin C	Fibre
72 cal	5.0 gm	13.7 gm	0.3 gm	357.3 mcg	9.0 mg	0.5 gm

❀ *Soya Cinnamon Custard with Fruits* ❀

Picture on page 75.

Suggested Serving Size Per Person: 1 serving

Here's a novel way to serve fruits to diabetics. Make a healthy custard with soya milk and low fat milk, flavour it with a dash of cinnamon and pour it over a selection of diabetes-friendly fruit like pears and apples. A simple but delectable sweet and fibre - filled snack is ready!

Preparation time: 10 minutes.   Cooking time: 10 to 15 minutes.   Serves 4.

2 cups mixed fruit cubes (papaya, pear, apple, melons, orange, gauva)
¼ cup pomegranate (*anar*)
2 tbsp chopped walnuts (*akhrot*)

For the soya cinnamon custard
½ cup soya milk
1½ tsp cornflour
½ cup low fat milk
A pinch of cinnamon (*dalchini*) powder
¾ tsp sugar substitute

For the soya cinnamon custard
1. Combine the cornflour with the soya milk in a bowl to make a smooth paste. Keep aside.
2. Boil the milk in a non-stick pan and add the corn flour- soya milk mixture to it while stirring continuously so that no lumps are formed.
3. Let the custard simmer for 2 to 3 minutes and add the cinnamon powder.
4. Remove from the flame, pour into a bowl and cool and keep aside.
5. Place it to chill in the refrigerator for 1 to 2 hours.
6. Divide the custard into 4 equal portions.

How to serve
1. Divide the fruits into 4 equal portions and put them in individual bowls.
2. Pour a portion of the custard over it.
   Serve immediately.

Nutritive values per serving

Energy	Protein	Carbohydrates	Fat	Calcium	Fibre
67 cal	2.2 gm	6.4 gm	3.7 gm	40.0 mg	0.7 gm

SOYA CINNAMON CUSTARD WITH FRUITS : Recipe on page 73. →

❄ *Bean Sprouts Stir-Fry* ❄

Suggested Serving Size Per Person: 1 serving

Bean sprouts are full of nutrients like fibre and vitamin C, which helps to improve the function of insulin (utilises glucose). Mix them with colourful vegetables to make a low calorie snack that is as tasty as it is nutritious. Remember to make the stir-fry on a very high flame to prevent mushrooms from letting out water.

Preparation time: 10 minutes.   Cooking time: 5 to 7 minutes.   Serves 4.

1 cup bean sprouts
1 cup sliced mushrooms (*khumbh*)
1 cup roughly chopped broccoli
½ cup thinly sliced capsicum
¼ cup sliced baby corn
2 tsp finely chopped garlic
2 tsp dried thyme
1½ tsp oil
Salt to taste

1. Heat the oil in a wok or *kadhai* on a high flame; add the garlic and stir for a minute.
2. Add the bean sprouts, mushrooms, broccoli, capsicum and baby corn and stir-fry over a high flame for a few seconds.
3. Add the thyme and salt and cook for 2 minutes.
   Serve hot.

Handy tip: Dried thyme is an Italian herb which available in most provision stores.

Nutritive values per serving

Energy	Protein	Carbohydrates	Fat	Vitamin C	Fibre
73 cal	4.3 gm	11.2 gm	1.6 gm	**20.7 mg**	**1.2 gm**

❀ *Papaya and Melon Tango* ❀

Suggested Serving Size Per Person: 1 small glass

Rich in vitamins A and C and fibre, papaya and melon combine to make a sweet, tangy and filling drink. Lemon juice peps up the flavour of this fruity delight. Choose fully ripe fruits to do away with the need for a sugar substitute. Remember a home-made juice is always better than the store-bought variety, even if it claims to be sugar-free.

Preparation time: 5 to 7 minutes.   Cooking time: Nil.   Makes 2 small glasses.

½ small papaya, peeled, deseeded and cut into pieces
1 small muskmelon (*kharbooja*), peeled and cut into pieces
½ tsp lemon juice

Other ingredients
Crushed ice to serve

1. Blend all the ingredients in a mixer using little water (if required) till smooth.
2. Strain the juice using a strainer or a muslin cloth.

3. Add the lemon juice and mix well.
4. Place some crushed ice in 2 small individual glasses and pour the juice over it. Serve immediately.

Nutritive values per small glass

Energy	Protein	Carbohydrates	Fat	Vitamin A	Vitamin C	Fibre
64 cal	1.2 gm	13.8 gm	0.5 gm	**995.1 mcg**	**105.8 mg**	**1.6 gm**

JAR SNACKS

It's a good idea to carry light snacks with you to combat a sudden onset of low blood sugar. Ideally you should keep such snacks in your purse or briefcase, in your office desk drawer, and in your gym bag. These snacks should provide not more than **100-150 calories per serving.**

Jar snacks are everyday snacks that are prepared in advance and stored in air-tight containers. However the usual deep-fried jar snacks like *puris*, crispies etc. are replaced with more healthy cooking methods such as baking and dry roasting. Make traditional snacks like *puris,* crispies, and *chivda* with diabetes-friendly ingredients like oats, cinnamon, *methi* and onions.

Suggested Serving Size Per Person here is equally important. Only **8 to 10 *Jowar Onion Puris, page 83*** or **3 *Oat and Cinnamon Cookies, page 88*, 2 *Spicy Phudina Khakhras, page 90*** are recommended. To relish these snacks to satisfy your mid-morning or mid-evening hunger pangs just reduce the serving rice to half i.e. have 4 to 5 Jowar Onion Puris or 1½ Oat and Cinnamon Cookies.

❀ Healthy Chivda ❀

Picture on page 2.

Suggested Serving Size Per Person: 1 serving

Yet another variation of a favourite Indian snack! Use oats and poha to make this healthy chivda. If suffering from high blood pressure, replace papad with oil free khakhras. Carry this snack in your bag to work or to the gym for an instant pick-me-up when you feel your blood sugar levels decreasing.

Preparation time: 5 minutes.   Cooking time: 20 minutes.   Serves 4.

1 cup roasted quick rolled oats
½ cup roasted *poha* (rice flakes)
1 *urad dal papad,* roasted and crushed
¼ cup roasted *chana dal* (*daria dal*)
¼ tsp mustard seeds (*rai / sarson*)
2 green chillies, slit lengthwise
6 to 8 curry leaves (*kadi patta*)
A pinch asafoetida (*hing*)
A pinch turmeric powder (*haldi*)

1 tsp powdered sugar
2 tsp oil
Salt to taste

1. Heat the oil in a non-stick pan, add the mustard seeds, green chillies and curry leaves and fry for some time.
2. When the seeds crackle, add the asafoetida and turmeric powder and mix well.
3. Add the oats, *poha, papad, chana dal,* sugar and salt and mix well. Cool and store in an air-tight container.

Nutritive values per serving

Energy	Protein	Carbohydrates	Fat	Zinc	Fibre
147 cal	**5.7 gm**	25.6 gm	4.6 gm	**0.2 mg**	**1.3 gm**

❀ *Jowar Onion Puris* ❀

Picture on page 85.

Suggested Serving Size Per Person: 8 to 10 small puris

Onions and sesame seeds add flavour to the otherwise bland iron and zinc-rich jowar flour used in these baked puris. At just 10 calories per puri, you can enjoy them without guilt! Make the puris in advance and keep them ready for those sudden hunger pangs.

Preparation time: 10 minutes.   Cooking time: Nil.   Makes 36 small *puris*.
Baking temperature: 180°C (360°F).   Baking time: 15 to 20 minutes.

½ cup *jowar* (white millet) flour
¼ cup chopped onions
2 tbsp black sesame seeds (*til*)
Salt to taste

Other ingredients
¼ tsp oil for greasing

1. Combine all the ingredients and knead into a firm dough using as much water as required.
2. Divide the dough into 36 equal portions and roll out each portion into a thin circle of 38 mm. (1.5") diameter.
3. Place these circles on a greased baking tray and prick all over using a fork.
4. Bake in a pre-heated oven at 180°C (360°F) for 10 to 15 minutes or till the *puris* are golden brown and crisp, turning them around once.
5. Cool and store in an air-tight container. These will stay fresh for 3-4 days.

Nutritive values per small *puri*

Energy	Protein	Carbohydrates	Fat	Calcium	Iron	Zinc	Fibre
10 cal	0.3 gm	1.2 gm	0.4 gm	8.8 mg	0.1 mg	0.1 mg	0.1 gm

JOWAR ONION PURIS : Recipe on page 83. →

❀ *Methi Crispies* ❀

Leafy vegetables do wonders for diabetics. Here they are mixed with whole wheat flour and soya flour to make a healthy snack, flavoured with sesame seeds and ajwain. Eat them with a low calorie dip of your choice or enjoy them with a cup of sugar-free tea.

Preparation time: 10 minutes.   Cooking time: 10 minutes.   Serves 4.
Baking temperature: 180°C (360°F).   Baking time: 18 to 20 minutes.

½ cup whole wheat flour (*gehun ka atta*)
¼ cup soya flour
¼ cup chopped fenugreek (*methi*) leaves
2 tbsp low fat curds (*dahi*), page 101
½ tsp sugar
2 tsp sesame seeds (*til*)
½ tsp cumin seeds (*jeera*)
¼ tsp *ajwain* (carom seeds)
2 tsp oil
Salt to taste

Other ingredients
¼ tsp oil for greasing

1. Combine all the ingredients together in a bowl and knead into a firm dough using enough water.
2. Divide the dough into 7 equal portions and roll out each portion into a thin round of 150 mm. (6″) diameter.
3. Heat a non-stick pan and gently cook each round on both sides till half done. Keep aside to cool.
4. Prick the cooled rounds with a fork at regular intervals.
5. Cut into small diamonds or squares and arrange on a greased baking tray.
6. Bake in a pre-heated oven at 180°C (360°F) for 12 to 15 minutes or till the squares are crisp and golden brown.
7. Cool and store in an air-tight container.

Nutritive values per serving

Energy	Protein	Carbohydrates	Fat	Iron	Fibre
113 cal	4.0 gm	11.6 gm	4.5 gm	1.2 mg	0.5 gm

❄ *Oat and Cinnamon Cookies* ❄

Suggested Serving Size Per Person: 3 cookies

Cinnamon helps utilise glucose in the body, preventing a redundant rise in blood glucose levels. It also blocks the formation of free radicals that can damage our body cells and cause complications like heart disorders and other diabetes related complications. Try these healthy cookies the next time you feel like nibbling something sweet.

Preparation time: 15 minutes.   Cooking time: Nil.   Makes 15 cookies.
Baking temperature: 150°C (300°F).   Baking time: 25 minutes.

½ cup quick rolled oats, roasted and coarsely powdered
½ cup whole wheat flour (*gehun ka atta*)
2½ tbsp low fat butter, softened
½ tsp cinnamon (*dalchini*) powder
1½ tsp sugar substitute
¼ tsp baking powder

1. Combine all the ingredients in a bowl, add enough water to make semi-soft dough.
   Do not knead much.

88

2. Roll out the dough in ¼" thickness and cut 15 cookies with a 75mm. (3") diameter round cookie cutter.
3. Bake in a pre-heated oven at 150°C (300°F) for 20 minutes, turning them upside down once in between.
4. Remove, cool and store in an air-tight container. These cookies will stay fresh for a week.

Nutritive values per cookie

Energy	Protein	Carbohydrates	Fat	Iron	Zinc	Fibre
33 cal	0.9 gm	4.3 gm	1.3 gm	0.3 mg	0.1 mg	0.2 gm

Spicy Phudina Khakhras

This Gujarati staple is traditionally made and served with a lot of ghee. Here is a healthier version made with only 1 tsp of oil. Mint and chillies add flavour to this popular snack, one of my favourites. Use innovative toppings for added taste. Carry them with you on your travels and you'll find it much easier to make new friends!

Preparation time: 10 minutes.   Cooking time: 15 minutes.   Makes 8 *khakhras*.

1 cup whole wheat flour (*gehun ka atta*)
½ cup mint leaves (*phudina*)
1 green chilli, finely chopped
½ tsp coarsely crushed roasted cumin seeds (*jeera*)
2 tsp oil
Salt to taste

Other ingredients
Whole wheat flour (*gehun ka atta*) for rolling

1. Grind together the mint leaves and green chillies with ¼ cup of water in a mixer.
2. Combine all the remaining ingredients in a bowl and knead into a soft dough using the mint water.
3. Divide the dough into 8 equal portions and roll out each portion into a very thin round of 125 mm. (5") diameter using a little flour.
4. Cook each round on a non-stick pan until brown spots appear on both the sides.
5. With the help of a folded muslin cloth, press the *khakhra* from all the sides and cook over a slow flame till it is crisp.
6. Cool and store in an air-tight container. These will stay fresh upto 15 days.

Nutritive values per *khakhra*

Energy	Protein	Carbohydrates	Fat	Vitamin A	Fibre
60 cal	1.8 gm	9.7 gm	1.6 gm	50.8 mcg	0.4 gm

ACCOMPANIMENTS

Store-bought sauces and dips are out of diabetic menus. Home-made alternatives are not only healthier, they certainly taste better as well. Avoid high fat ingredients such as groundnuts and coconut and opt for vegetables like onions, garlic, mint, etc. The recipes here make wonderful accompaniments for most of the snacks like *Moong Dal Idlis, page 10, Buckwheat Pancakes, page 12 and Karela Tikkis, page 22* etc. in this book.

❀ Mint and Onion Chutney ❀

Picture on back cover.

Suggested Serving Size Per Person: 1 tbsp

Onions impart sweetness while lemon juice perks up the flavour of this piquant chutney.
Mint and coriander provide vitamin A and C, making this an ideal accompaniment for your
favourite snacks. Make the chutney in advance and store in the freezer for up to six days.
Goes well with Soyabean Pancakes, page 24, or to make sandwiches such as the
Club Sandwich, page 49.

Preparation time: 5 to 7 minutes.   Cooking time: Nil.
Makes 1 cup (approx. 14 tbsp).

2 cups chopped mint leaves *(phudina)*
1 cup chopped coriander *(dhania)*
¾ cup sliced onions
Juice of 1 to 2 lemons
1 tsp sugar *(optional)*
2 to 3 green chillies
Salt to taste

1. Combine all the ingredients and blend to a smooth paste in a mixer using very little water.
2. Store refrigerated in an air-tight container and use as required.

Nutritive values per tbsp

Energy	Protein	Carbohydrates	Fat	Vitamin A	Vitamin C	Calcium	Fibre
9 cal	0.3 gm	1.7 gm	0.1 gm	193.0 mcg	4.8 mg	14.9 mg	0.2 gm

❄ *Garlic Tomato Chutney* ❄

Picture on page 1.

Suggested Serving Size Per Person: 1 tbsp

Wonder ingredient garlic contains 'allicin' which combines with vitamin B_1 (thiamine) to activate the function of the pancreas and promote insulin secretion. While garlic is effective in the prevention or cure of diabetes, tomatoes provide adequate vitamin A (74.1 mcg per tbsp). 1 tbsp of this chutney is enough to add interest to Adai, page 14 or Karela Tikkis, page 22.

Preparation time: 10 minutes.   Cooking time: 15 minutes.
Makes ¾ cup (approx. 11 tbsp).

6 to 8 large cloves garlic, finely chopped
1 cup finely chopped tomatoes
2 whole dry red chilies, soaked in ¼ cup water
¼ cup chopped spring onion whites
1 tbsp finely chopped spring onion greens
1 tbsp finely chopped coriander (*dhania*)
1 tsp olive oil / oil
Salt to taste

1. Drain the soaked chillies and chop them finely. Keep aside.
2. Heat the oil in a non-stick pan, add the spring onion whites and garlic and sauté over a slow flame for 4 to 5 minutes till they are lightly brown.
3. Add the chillies and salt and sauté again.
4. Add the tomatoes and cook for 10 to 12 minutes over a slow flame till the tomatoes are soft and can be mashed lightly.
5. Cool completely and add the spring onion greens and coriander and mix well. Serve chilled or at room temperature.
6. Store refrigerated in an air-tight container and use as required.

Nutritive values per tbsp

Energy	Protein	Carbohydrates	Fat	Vitamin A	Fibre
9 cal	0.2 gm	0.9 gm	0.5 gm	**74.1 mcg**	**0.3 gm**

❃ *Healthy Coconut Chutney* ❃

Picture on page 19.

Suggested Serving Size Per Person: 1 tbsp

Coconut is high in saturated (bad) fats that cause obesity and heart diseases and aggravate diabetes. Reduce the quantity of coconut you normally use and add roasted urad dal and roasted chana dal for healthier, tastier chutney. Best accompaniment for Mini Moong Dal Idlis, page 10, Masala Wheat Dosa, page 18.

Preparation time: 10 minutes.   Cooking time: 15 minutes.
Makes 1 cup (approx. 14 tbsp).

¼ cup grated fresh coconut
½ cup chopped coriander (*dhania*)
2 tbsp roasted *chana dal* (*daria dal*)
1 tbsp *urad dal* (split black gram)
2 small green chillies, chopped
1 tsp grated ginger

For the tempering
1 tsp mustard seeds (*rai / sarson*)

1 whole dry red chilli, broken into pieces
2 to 3 curry leaves (*kadi patta*)
A pinch asafoetida (*hing*)
1 tsp oil

Other ingredients
½ tsp oil for roasting

1. Heat the oil in a non-stick pan and lightly roast the *chana* and *urad dals* and stir till they turn crisp and brown. Keep aside to cool.
2. When cool, blend the *dals* in a mixer to a fine powder.
3. Add the coconut, coriander, green chillies, ginger and salt to it and blend to a smooth paste 2 tbsp of water. Keep aside.
4. For the tempering, heat the oil in a small non-stick pan, add the mustard seeds, red chilli and curry leaves. Sauté till the seeds crackle and add the asafoetida.
5. Pour this tempering over the *chutney* and mix well.
6. Store refrigerated in an air-tight container and use as required.

Nutritive values per tbsp

Energy	Protein	Carbohydrates	Fat	Iron	Fibre
25 cal	0.8 gm	2.2 gm	1.4 gm	0.2 mg	0.2 gm

❁ *Carrot Garlic Chutney* ❁

Suggested Serving Size Per Person: 1 tbsp

Home-made vegetable chutneys are a better option than store-bought sauces and dips, which tend to be highly salted. Carrots subtly flavoured with garlic, chilli powder and lemon juice makes a mouth-watering accompaniment for Buckwheat Pancakes, page 12.

Preparation time: 10 minutes.   Cooking time: Nil.
Makes ½ cup (approx. 7 tbsp).

1 cup thickly grated carrots
2 tbsp chopped garlic
2 tbsp chilli powder

¼ tsp lemon juice
1 tsp oil
Salt to taste

1. Blend the garlic, chilli powder, lemon juice and salt to a fine paste in a mixer.
2. Pour into a bowl, add the carrots and oil and mix well.
3. Store refrigerated in an air-tight container and use as required.

Nutritive values per tbsp

Energy	Protein	Carbohydrates	Fat	Vitamin A	Fibre
13 cal	0.1 gm	1.4 gm	0.7 gm	**244.0 mcg**	0.2 gm

BASIC RECIPES

We use milk and milk products like curds, *paneer* liberally in our daily diet. Though rich in nutrients like protein and calcium they are also high in calories and saturated fat, the very fact that is always unobserved. To help cut down on the fat from dairy products all you have to do is switch to their low fat counterparts. Not only they taste the same and are equally good sources of protein and calcium but also provide lesser calories and fat. Low fat milk is easily available in the market as 99.9% fat free under different brand names. Use this milk preferably as it is low in calories and fat. If you don't find it, you can use double-toned milk (slightly high in fat compared to 99.9% fat free milk).

Alternately you can make low fat milk at home. Preparing low fat milk at home does not demand much effort, all you need to do is boil the milk and skim the fat (*malai*) that is formed after the milk cols. Repeat this procedure at least twice or thrice a day to get almost fat-free milk.

You can use this milk to prepare low fat curds and *paneer* and use them in the recipes to make them low in calories like we have used in ***Buckwheat Pancakes, page 12, Paneer Veggie Wrap, page 45, Jamun Smoothie, page 71*** etc.

❉ Low Fat Curds ❉

Made from low fat milk (99.9% fat free), low fat curds provide only 71 calories and 0.2 fat per cup. Use without guilt in recipes like Buckwheat Pancakes, page 12 or Methi Crispies, page 86 or serve plain with Stuffed Nachni Rotis, page 26. Also use low fat curds to make low fat paneer, page 102.

Preparation time: 5 minutes.   Cooking time: 2 minutes.   Makes 5 cups.
Setting time: 5 to 6 hours.

1 litre low fat milk (readily available in the market)
1 tbsp curds (*dahi*)

1. Warm the milk.
2. Add the curds, mix well and cover.
3. Keep aside until the curds set (approx. 5 to 6 hours).
4. During the cold climate, place inside a casserole or closed oven to set.

Nutritive values per cup

Energy	Protein	Carbohydrates	Fat	Calcium	Fibre
71 cal	**7.1 gm**	10.2 gm	0.2 gm	**304.5 mg**	**0.0 gm**

❋ *Low Fat Paneer (Cottage Cheese)* ❋

Use low fat milk to make this low calorie version of paneer. Add low fat curds instead of lemon juice to obtain a relatively larger quantity of softer paneer. Low fat paneer works well in recipes like Spicy Paneer on Toast, page 30, Paneer Veggie Wrap, page 45 etc.

Preparation time: 30 minutes.   Cooking time: 10 minutes.
Makes 70 grams (approx. ½ cup).

3 cups low fat milk (readily available in the market)
1½ cups low fat curds (*dahi*), page 101, beaten

1. Put the milk to boil in a broad non-stick pan. When it starts boiling, add the curds and mix well.
2. Remove from the heat and stir gently until the milk curdles.
3. Strain and tie the curdled milk in a muslin cloth. Hang for about half an hour to allow the whey to drain out.
4. Use as required.

Nutritive values for ½ cup

Energy	Protein	Carbohydrates	Fat	Calcium	Fibre
315 cal	**31.5 gm**	45.0 gm	0.2 gm	**304.5 mg**	**0.0 gm**